QUICK CALCULATION

Move any single digit from one column to any other column so that the numbers in all three columns add up to the same amount.

Illustration: Marc Nadel

A	B	C
1	4	7
2	5	8
3	6	9
6	15	24

Answer on page 48

Hint on page 46

3

Add up the numbers on the matching shapes to fill in the amount each diner ordered from the menu.

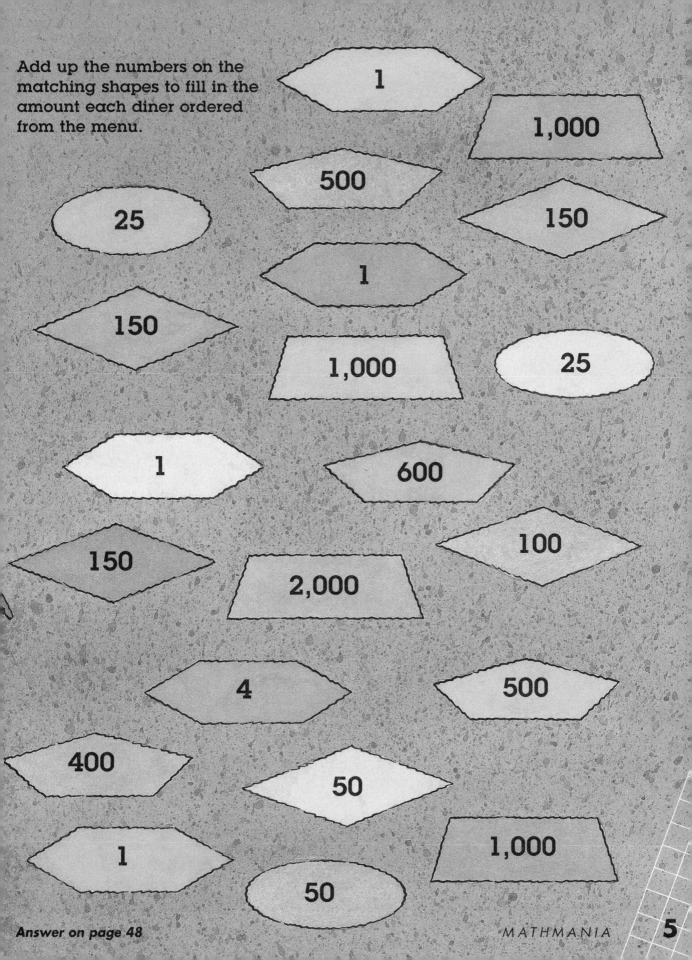

1

1,000

500

25

150

1

150

1,000

25

1

600

150

2,000

100

4

500

400

50

1

1,000

50

LAST COIN

Each child needs just one more coin in order to make a $1.00. Match one of the coins in the plate to one of the piles on the table.

Answer on page 48

CALL TO ORDER

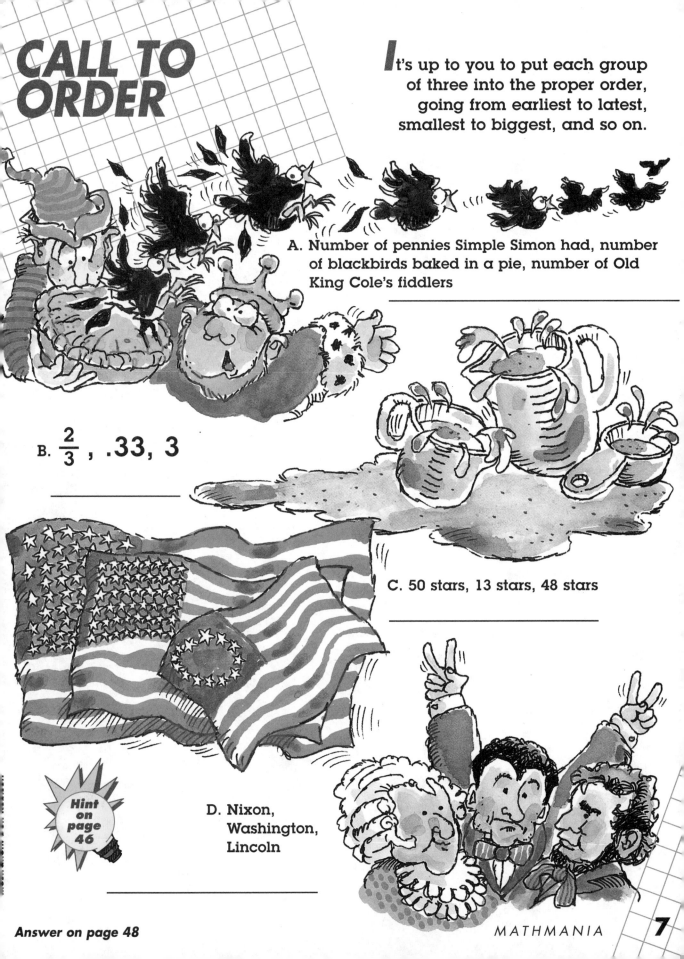

It's up to you to put each group of three into the proper order, going from earliest to latest, smallest to biggest, and so on.

A. Number of pennies Simple Simon had, number of blackbirds baked in a pie, number of Old King Cole's fiddlers

_____

B. $\frac{2}{3}$, .33, 3

_____

C. 50 stars, 13 stars, 48 stars

_____

Hint on page 46

D. Nixon, Washington, Lincoln

_____

PERIMETERS

The perimeter of an object is the measurement of its outer edges. For instance, if each side of a square measures 1 inch, the perimeter is 4 inches (1 + 1 + 1 + 1). To solve our riddle, you'll need to find the perimeter of each figure shown. Measurements are given

Answer on page 48

for most sides, and sides of equal length within each figure are marked with notches. Once you've found all the perimeters, look for the matching numbers beneath the blanks. Put the letters from the figures in the blanks with the matching perimeters, and you'll have the answer to the riddle in no time.

Hint on page 46

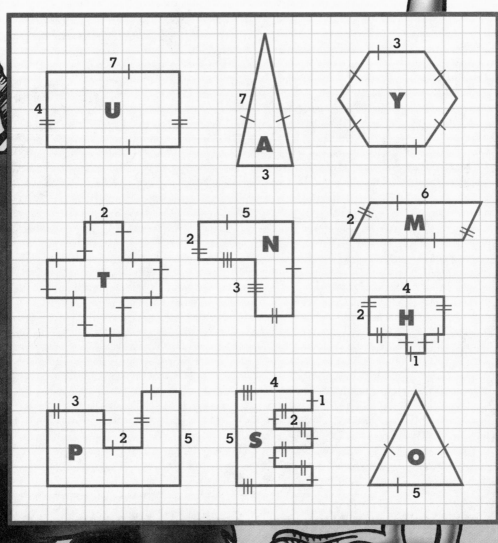

What large animal can put you into a trance?

$$\overline{}_{17} \ \overline{}_{14} \ \overline{}_{18} \ \overline{}_{28} \ \overline{}_{20} \ \overline{}_{15} \ \text{-} \ \overline{}_{28} \ \overline{}_{15} \ \overline{}_{24} \ \overline{}_{17} \ \overline{}_{16} \ \overline{}_{22} \ \overline{}_{26}$$

Illustration: Jerry Zimmerman

ON THE RUN

Lydia, Maureen, and Nancy are running laps to prepare for the big track meet. Can you use the clues to tell how many laps each runner ran?

Answer on page 48

Illustration: Anni Matsick

Lydia and Maureen ran a total of 12 laps.

Maureen and Nancy ran a total of 18 laps.

Lydia and Nancy ran a total of 10 laps.

Hint on page 46

DOTS A LOT

Keep a sharp eye out as you connect these dots in numerical order.

Answer on page 48

Illustration: Joe Wigfield

CROSSWORD RIDDLE

Fill in these boxes with the letters of the words that answer each clue or description. When you've completed the grid, rearrange the letters of each word in the yellow and blue boxes to discover the answer to our riddle.

ACROSS

1. Number of decades in two centuries
6. The opposite of a high number is a _____ one.
7. This prefix means "two," as before *cycle* or *plane*.
8. Frozen H_2O
10. Poems
12. Abbreviation for *avenue*
14. *One* in Spanish
16. 4 is in this place in the number 649.
19. Number of people in a duet
21. Short form of *advertisement*
22. A period of historic time
24. Number of inches in one foot

DOWN

1. This prefix means "three," as before *cycle* or *plane*.
2. The roman numeral XI stands for this number.
3. Abbreviation for *number*
4. Dickens story: *A Tale of _____ Cities*, or 9 – 7
5. Card game: Go _____
7. Don't _____ late.
9. Abbreviation for *California*
11. Word before *floss*
13. A really good film is called a four-_____ movie.
15. Expression of pain
17. Short form of *Edward*
18. To stitch things together
20. Earth has this number of moons.
23. This prefix means "to do again," as before *cycle* or *gain*.

Answer on page 48

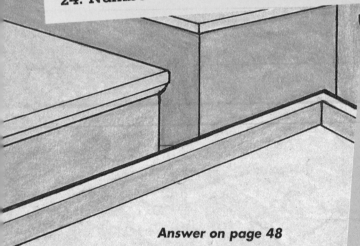

What can you find in every single yard?

□ □ □ □ □　□ □ □ □

Illustration: Rick Geary

13

HOT DOG!

Four boys and three girls entered a hot-dog-eating contest at the local fair. Can you follow the clues to figure out how many hot dogs each person ate, as well as who was the winner?

Illustration: Doug Cushman

HOT-DOG-EATING CONTEST

Hint on page 46

1. Timmy ate twice as many hot dogs as Todd.
2. Tanya and Todd tied, eating the same number of hot dogs.
3. Tina was full after eating only four hot dogs.
4. Tony ate as many hot dogs as all three girls combined.
5. Terri ate three times as many hot dogs as Tina, but only half as many as Ted, who ate one fewer than Tony.

MATHMANIA

Answer on page 48

FAMOUS NAME

If you connect the dots in the order listed, you will find the name of the person described in this autobiography.

I was born Elizabeth Griscom in Philadelphia in 1752. It was my fame as a seamstress that brought a famous general to my house with a very rough sketch for a flag. I turned that flag into a reality, and soon the stars-and-stripes design was adopted by Congress as the official flag of the United States.

```
        A   B   C   D   E   F   G   H   I   J   K   L
    1   .   .   .   .   .   .   .   .   .   .   .   .
    2   .   .   .   .   .   .   .   .   .   .   .   .
    3   .   .   .   .   .   .   .   .   .   .   .   .
    4   .   .   .   .   .   .   .   .   .   .   .   .
    5   .   .   .   .   .   .   .   .   .   .   .   .
    6   .   .   .   .   .   .   .   .   .   .   .   .
```

A1-B1 C1-D1 E1-G1 H1-I1 A4-B4 C4-D4 E4-F4 G4-H4
A3-B3 C3-D3 H3-I3 C6-D6 E6-F6 G6-H6 A2-B2 C2-D2
H2-I2 A5-B5 E5-F5 G5-H5 A1-A3 B1-B3 C1-C3 F1-F3
H1-H2 J1-K2 A4-A6 B4-B5 C4-C6 D4-D6 E4-E5 G4-G5
I2-I3 K2-K3 A5-B6 F5-F6 H5-H6 L1-K2

Illustration: Kit Wray

Answer on page 49

PENCIL THEM IN

Jeremy is organizing his pencils into three different categories: pencils that have the color yellow on them, pencils with erasers, and pencils that are sharpened. You can help sort these by placing the letter identifying each pencil into the proper spot on his diagram.

The places where two or more circles overlap are for those pencils that have two or more of the same characteristics. For example, one pencil might be sharpened and yellow. The letter for that pencil would go in the spot where those two circles overlap. Not all pencils will go in a circle.

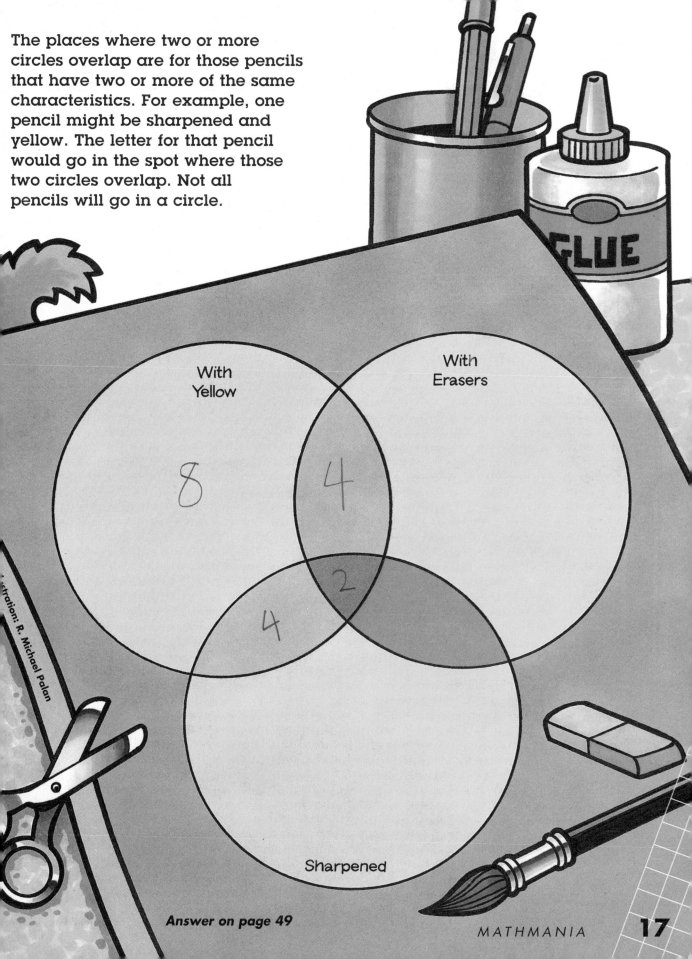

With Yellow

With Erasers

8

4

2

4

Sharpened

Answer on page 49

DIFFERENT DEFINITIONS

You'll have to figure out our definition of today's word one column at a time. Find the letters described by each clue. Then print the letters in the blanks, going from left to right in order.

First $\frac{1}{2}$ of WHEN
Final $\frac{1}{3}$ of WOMBAT
First $\frac{1}{2}$ of INFINITY
Final $\frac{3}{4}$ of WELD
Middle $\frac{3}{5}$ of VERSE
Final $\frac{3}{4}$ of RUSE
First $\frac{4}{5}$ of TOKEN

Final $\frac{3}{4}$ of KEPT
First $\frac{1}{2}$ of HEIGHT
Middle $\frac{1}{3}$ of HARBOR
Final $\frac{5}{6}$ of WREATH
First $\frac{3}{4}$ of FREE
First $\frac{1}{2}$ of SHUT

Today's word: **BASEMENT**

_ _ _ _ _ _ _ _ _ _ _

_ _ _ _ _ _ _ _ _ _ _

_ _ _ _ _ _ _ _ _ _

Answer on page 49

Hint on page 46

Illustration: Don Robison

TICKET TIME

This busy travel agent wrote down some notes to help him remember who ordered which ticket. Can you put the right name on each ticket?

1. Jen has $400 to spend.
2. Sean wants to go on two vacations for a total of $750.
3. Brooke can spend $50 more than Sean.
4. Jeff hates the cold.
5. Felix will go anywhere.

A. Travel to the best beach $484

B. Fly to World Mall $300

C. Ski the slopes $521

D. Sail away for a day $266

E. Backpack the Molehill Mountains $700

F. Bunk at Dudley's Dude Ranch $800

Illustration: Bill Colrus

Hint on page 46

Answer on page 49

A TOUGH SPELL

Each of the 50 states had a spelling bee. Now it's up to you as the United States Spelling Supervisor to find a day in November to hold

Answer on page 49

SPELLING BEE STATE FINALS

the National Spelling Bee. Unfortunately, 12 of the states have certain restrictions. You need to find a day that is good for all the states.

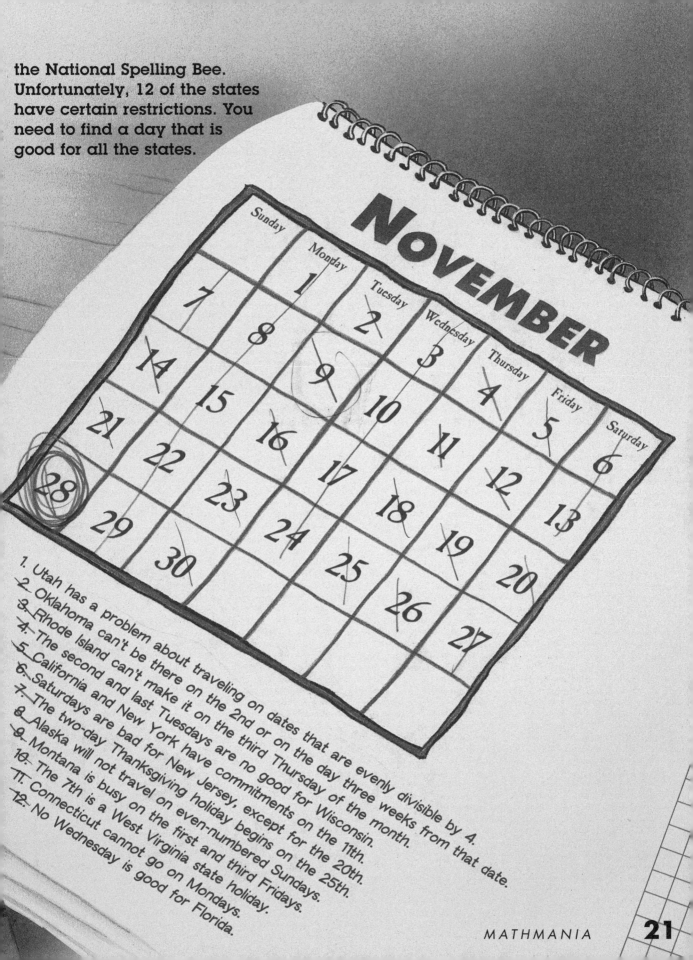

NOVEMBER

Sunday	Monday	Tuesday	Wednesday	Thursday	Friday	Saturday
7	1	2	3	4	5	6
14	8	9	10	11	12	13
21	15	16	17	18	19	20
28	22	23	24	25	26	27
	29	30				

1. Utah has a problem about traveling on dates that are evenly divisible by 4.
2. Oklahoma can't be there on the 2nd or on the day three weeks from that date.
3. Rhode Island can't make it on the third Thursday of the month.
4. The second and last Tuesdays are no good for Wisconsin.
5. California and New York have commitments on the 11th.
6. Saturdays are bad for New Jersey, except for the 20th.
7. The two-day Thanksgiving holiday begins on the 25th.
8. Alaska will not travel on even-numbered Sundays.
9. Montana is busy on the first and third Fridays.
10. The 7th is a West Virginia state holiday.
11. Connecticut cannot go on Mondays.
12. No Wednesday is good for Florida.

DIGIT DOES IT

That amazing investigator, Inspector Digit, is wrapping up his latest case. Someone had been removing all the pens from the post offices around the city. Digit managed

Hint on page 47

Illustration: Joe Boddy

to catch a suspect, but he needs help putting together the case. The only clue is this note. Can you decode the message and help put the Inspector on the right track?

¯¯ ¯¯ ¯ ¯¯   ¯ ¯¯ ¯¯ ¯¯ ¯ ¯¯ ¯¯ ¯ ¯¯   ¯¯ ¯ ¯ ¯ ¯¯,
12 2 1 10   3 13 22 20 2 17 14 4 10   12 3 8 3 14

¯ ¯ ¯   ¯¯ ¯ ¯   ¯¯ ¯ ¯¯ ¯   ¯¯ ¯   ¯ ¯¯
6 4 5   16 1 6   21 1 19 2   16 2   3 13

¯¯ ¯¯ ¯   ¯¯ ¯ ¯¯,   ¯ ¯ ¯¯   ¯¯ ¯¯ ¯ ¯¯
14 21 2   20 2 13   7 5 14   14 21 1 14

¯¯ ¯ ¯¯ ¯¯   ¯¯ ¯¯ ¯ ¯ ¯¯   ¯¯ ¯   ¯¯ ¯ ¯¯ ¯ ¯ ¯¯
11 4 13 14   22 14 1 3 13   16 6   17 1 10 2 2 10

¯ ¯ ¯   ¯¯ ¯ ¯¯ ¯   ¯¯ ¯   ¯ ¯¯ ¯¯ ¯ ¯ ¯¯ ¯
6 4 5   21 1 19 2   13 4   3 13 18 9 3 13 8

¯¯ ¯¯ ¯ ¯¯ ¯   ¯¯ ¯   ¯¯ ¯ ¯¯ ¯¯   ¯ ¯ ¯
11 21 2 10 2   14 4   15 3 13 12   1 9 9

E I   ¯¯ ¯ ¯¯ ¯¯   ¯ ¯ ¯   ¯¯ ¯ ¯ ¯¯
       20 2 13 22   6 4 5   13 2 2 12

¯¯ ¯ ¯¯   ¯ ¯¯ ¯ ¯¯ ¯ ¯¯ ¯¯ ¯.
15 4 10   2 19 3 12 2 13 17 2

¯¯ ¯ ¯ ¯   ¯¯ ¯ ¯ ¯¯ ¯¯
20 1 5 9   20 4 3 13 14

SLEEP TIGHT

Arlene is keeping a journal for her health class. She must keep track of the amount of sleep she gets each night for a week. Her teacher recommended that each student should get at least 10 hours of sleep a night. Can you tell how many hours of sleep Arlene got each night? What was her total number of hours of sleep for the week? How many days did she get at least 10 hours of sleep?

DAY	WENT TO BED	WOKE UP	HOURS OF SLEEP
Sunday	8:30 p.m.	6:00 a.m.	
Monday	9:00 p.m.	7:15 a.m.	
Tuesday	8:45 p.m.	7:00 a.m.	
Wednesday	9:30 p.m.	7:00 a.m.	
Thursday	8:15 p.m.	6:30 a.m.	
Friday	9:00 p.m.	6:00 a.m.	
Saturday	9:45 p.m.	7:30 a.m.	
		TOTAL	

Illustration: Doug Cushman

Answer on page 49

STEP BY STEP

Figure out the number sequence to find a path out of this maze. The sequence begins with 0, 9, and 4. Your path will lead you through each number only once, and your path will not cross over itself. Draw a line from number to number until you work your way out.

Hint on page 47

OUT

36	45	68	77	69	60
41	40	73	64	65	56
32	49	44	48	52	61
37	25	53	57	9	0
28	20	16	17	8	4
33	24	29	21	12	13

IN

Illustration: Marc Nadel

Answer on page 49

SCRAMBLED PICTURE

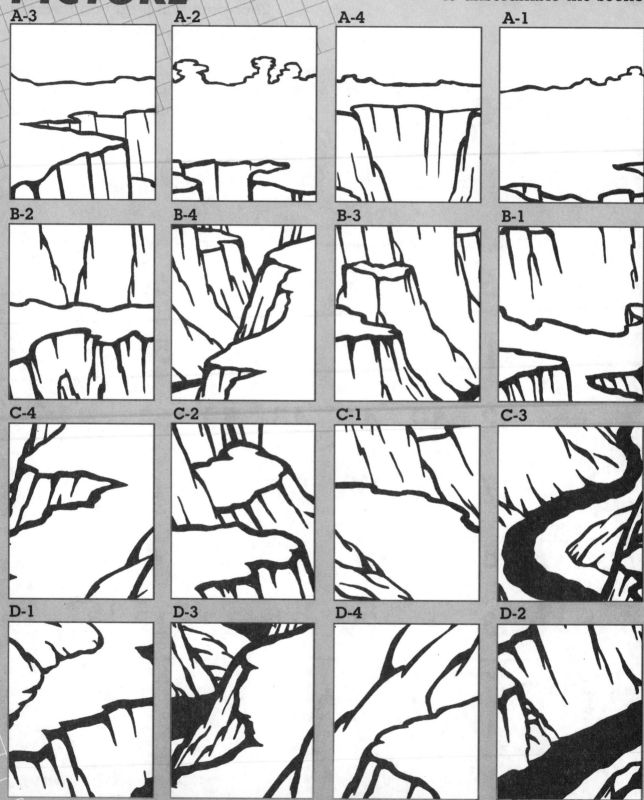

A-3 A-2 A-4 A-1

B-2 B-4 B-3 B-1

C-4 C-2 C-1 C-3

D-1 D-3 D-4 D-2

The letters and numbers tell
you where each rectangle
belongs. We've done the first
one, A-3, to start you off.

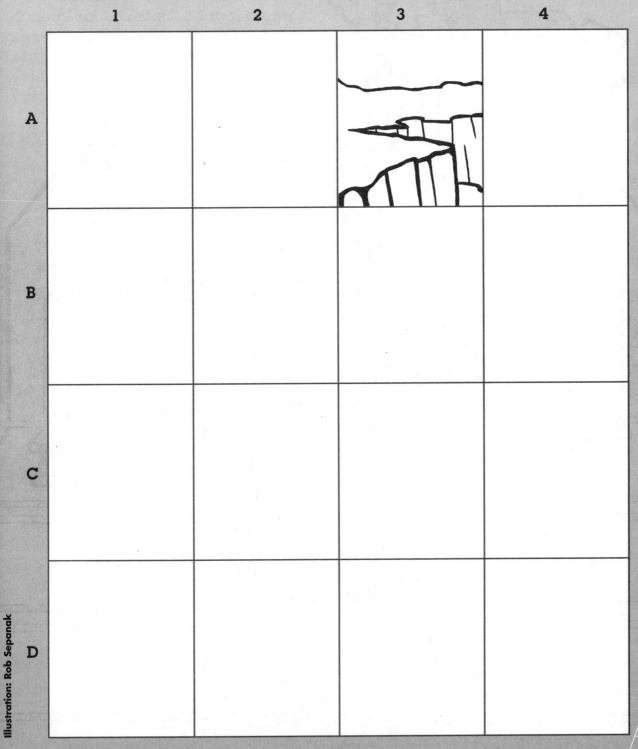

Answer on page 49

Illustration: Rob Sepanak

STACKING STANLEY

Stanley has to unpack cartons of books and stack them in the back room. He must put the books from each carton in even stacks, and each stack must contain the number of books asked for in each area. Can you look at the number of books on each carton and figure out the area in which Stanley should stack those books?

276 copies of
King Minus

169 copies of
*The Grapes
of Math*

152 copies of
Great Multiplications

994 copies of
*The Brothers
Addemup*

119 copies of
Alice in Integerland

220 copies of
The Indivisible Man

10 books
in each stack

12 books
in each stack

13 books
in each stack

14 books
in each stack

17 books
in each stack

19 books
in each stack

Hint
on
page
47

HAY, SAM

Sam runs a haying service in the summer. She has 24 customers. She bought 5 gallons of gas this morning. Her tractor, which is now empty, gets 6 miles to the gallon.

Answer on page 50

GASOLINE
5 GALLONS

Illustration: Rick Geary

Sam plans to hay 12 of the fields, which are 1 mile each, in the morning. After lunch, she will do $\frac{1}{4}$ of the total number of fields, which are $1\frac{1}{2}$ miles each. Then she will do the remaining fields, which are 2 miles each.

The problem is, does Sam have enough gas to hay all the fields?

Hint on page 47

MAGIC SQUARE

If you complete each problem in these small squares, the answers will give you a magic square. A magic square is one in which all the numbers in each row and every column,

Illustration: Jim Paillot

as well as the two diagonals, add up to the same amount. The answers in the small squares will include all the numbers from 2 through 26.

$16 \div 4 =$	$9 + 7 =$	$10 + 15 =$	$63 \div 9 =$	$9 \times 2 =$
$11 \times 2 =$	$24 \div 3 =$	$23 - 4 =$	$42 \div 7 =$	$5+5+5 =$
$6+7+8 =$	$5 \times 1 =$	$21 - 9 =$	$18 + 5 =$	$72 \div 8 =$
$9 + 4 =$	$3 \times 8 =$	$6 + 5 =$	$5 \times 4 =$	$24 \div 12 =$
$2 + 3 + 5 =$	$20 - 3 =$	$16 - 13 =$	$14 - 0 =$	$13 + 13 =$

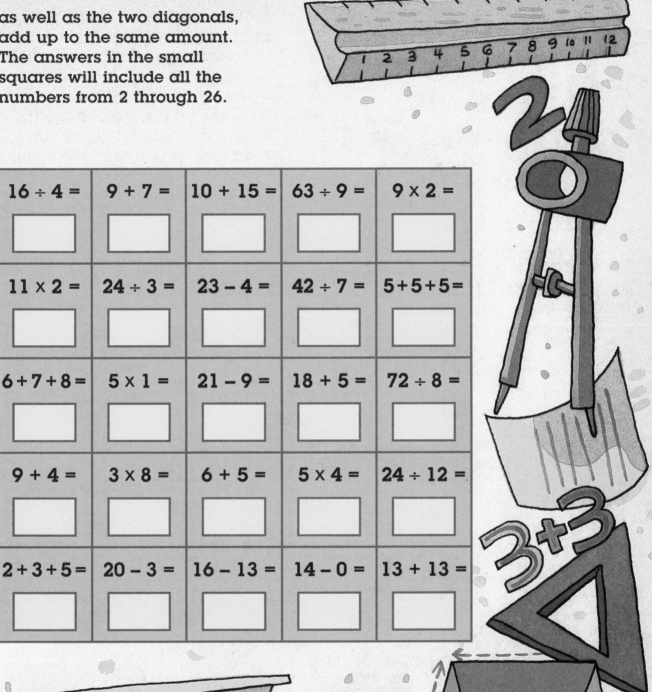

Answer on page 50

LIBRARY LAUGHS

Dewey has some funny books in his library. To check one out, solve each problem. Then go to the shelves to find the volume with the number that matches each answer. Put the matching letter in the blank beside each answer. Read down the letters you've filled in to find the title and author of the book Dewey just finished reading.

Illustration: Scott Peck

$27 \div 9 =$ _____

$3 \times 5 =$ _____

$26 - 3 =$ _____

$44 \div 22 =$ _____

$9 + 6 =$ _____

$50 \div 2 =$ _____

$22 - 4 =$ _____

$30 \div 2 =$ _____

$9 + 7 =$ _____

$14 - 9 =$ _____

$2 \times 10 =$ _____

$14 + 4 =$ _____

$18 \div 2 =$ _____

$9 - 6 =$ _____

$7 + 4 =$ _____

$26 - 7 =$ _____

$8 - 6 =$ _____

$5 \times 5 =$ _____

$24 \div 2 =$ _____

$19 - 18 =$ _____

$6 \times 3 =$ _____

$36 \div 2 =$ _____

$21 + 4 =$ _____

$10 \div 2 =$ _____

$5 \times 4 =$ _____

$24 - 4 =$ _____

Answer on page 50

PRECISE ICE

Re-create this image without crossing over any lines or removing your pencil from the page.

Illustration: Barbara Gray

CAN YOU CANOE?

Angie and her brother, Jacob, took a canoe trip for the day. Their guide, Hank, had planned the trip well, but a few unplanned

Hint on page 47

Answer on page 50

HANK

2701 HANK'S

HANK'S CANOES

Illustration: Scott Peck

34

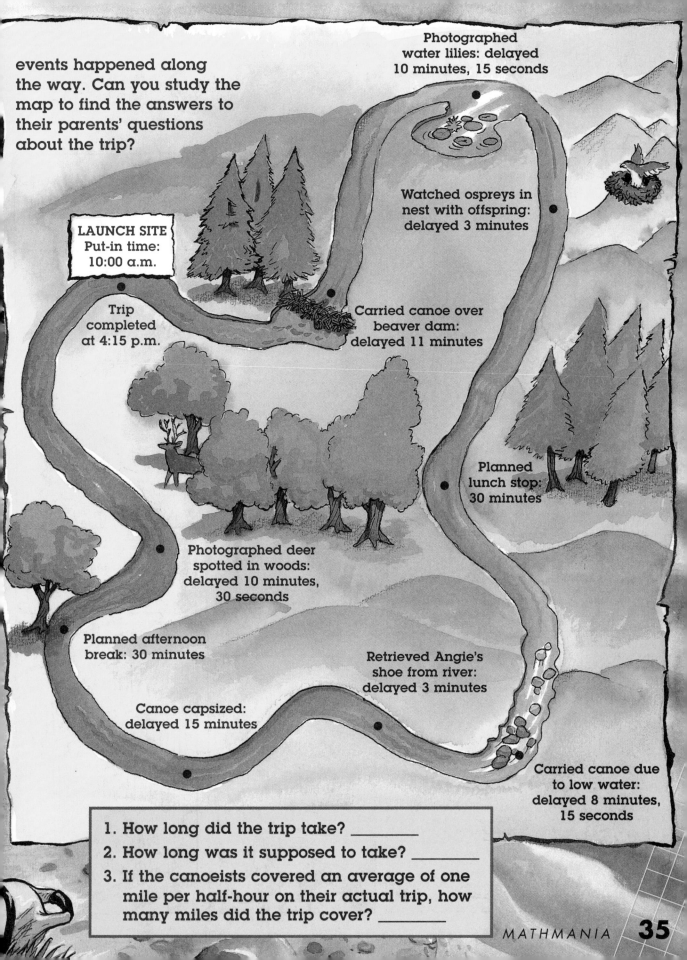

events happened along the way. Can you study the map to find the answers to their parents' questions about the trip?

Photographed water lilies: delayed 10 minutes, 15 seconds

Watched ospreys in nest with offspring: delayed 3 minutes

LAUNCH SITE
Put-in time:
10:00 a.m.

Trip completed at 4:15 p.m.

Carried canoe over beaver dam: delayed 11 minutes

Planned lunch stop: 30 minutes

Photographed deer spotted in woods: delayed 10 minutes, 30 seconds

Planned afternoon break: 30 minutes

Retrieved Angie's shoe from river: delayed 3 minutes

Canoe capsized: delayed 15 minutes

Carried canoe due to low water: delayed 8 minutes, 15 seconds

1. How long did the trip take? _____

2. How long was it supposed to take? _____

3. If the canoeists covered an average of one mile per half-hour on their actual trip, how many miles did the trip cover? _____

MATHMAGIC

Get ready
to blast off.

Get a friend to choose any number from 1 to 10. Ask him to multiply the number by 3.

Next, ask him to multiply the new total by 2, then again by 1, and then again by 0.

Now ask him to add 999 to his current total. Have him divide the new number by 3.

PHASES OF THE MOON

Then he should subtract 12 from the new total. Now ask him to read off his current answer, one number at a time.

When he says the final number, you should be able to yell, "Blast off!"

Turn to page 50 to find out why.

PLANETARIUM

COLOR BY NUMBERS

KEY
1 dot—Blue
2 dots—Turquoise
3 dots—Green
4 dots—Yellow
5 dots—Orange
6 dots—Black
7 dots—White

*U*se the key to color the spaces and you'll see a great light.

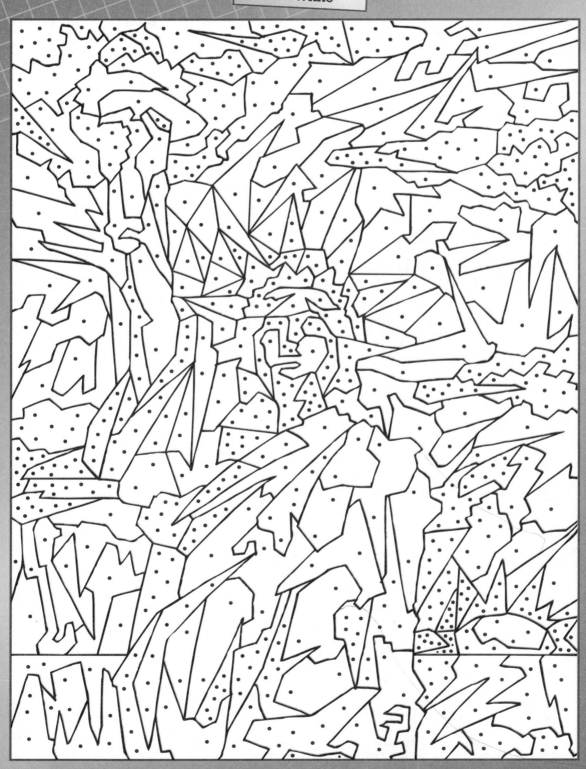

Illustration: Joe Wigfield

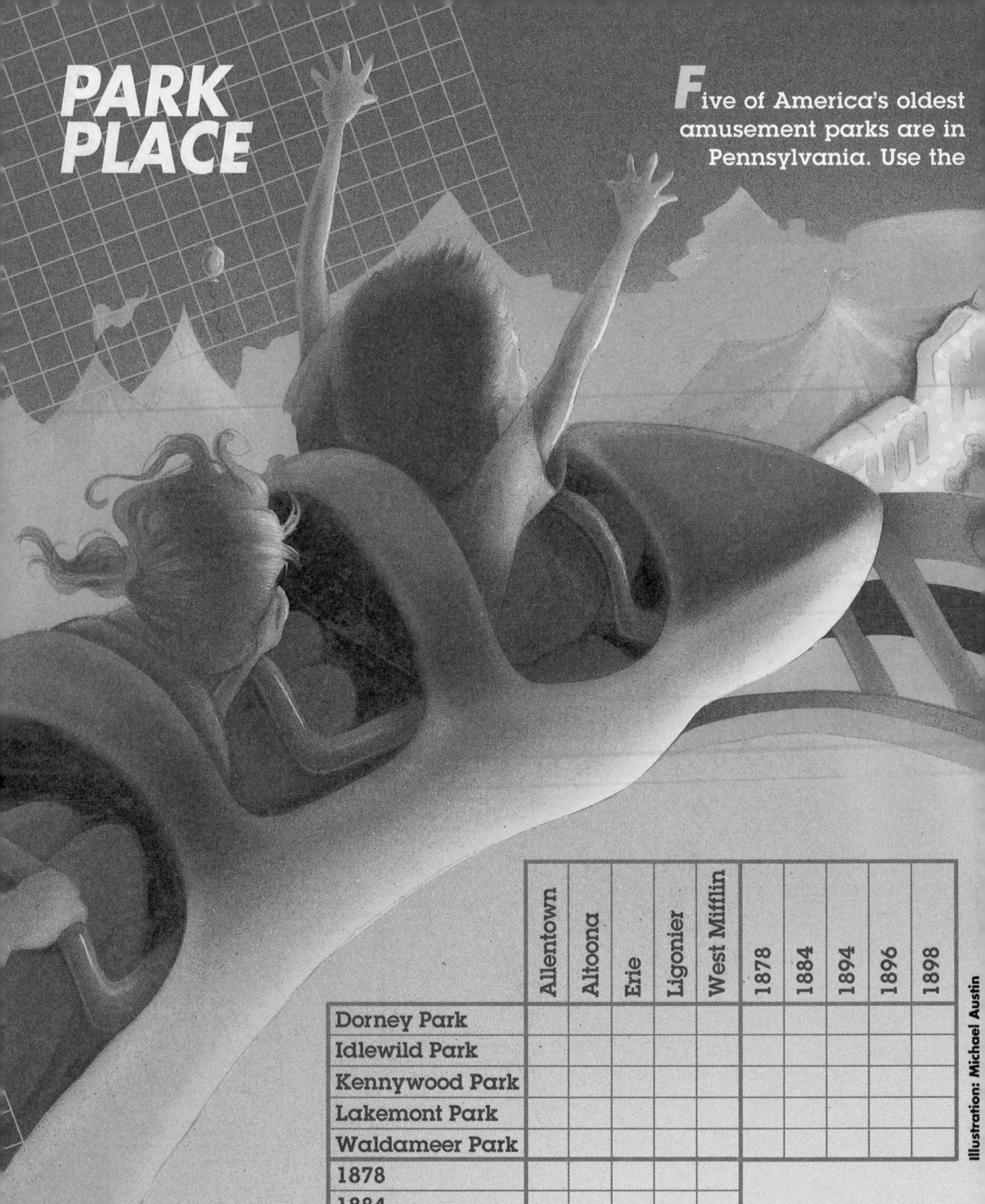

PARK PLACE

Five of America's oldest amusement parks are in Pennsylvania. Use the

	Allentown	Altoona	Erie	Ligonier	West Mifflin	1878	1884	1894	1896	1898
Dorney Park										
Idlewild Park										
Kennywood Park										
Lakemont Park										
Waldameer Park										
1878										
1884										
1894										
1896										
1898										

Illustration: Michael Austin

Answer on page 51

clues to figure out the year each park opened and where it is located.

The grid will help you keep track of the information. Put an *O* in a box where the information from the row and column agree. Put an *X* in a box where the information does not agree. Once you have an *O* box, the remaining boxes in that same row and column can all get *X*s.

1. The name of the oldest amusement park begins with a vowel, but it is not located in a town that begins with a vowel.

2. The amusement parks in Altoona and Allentown were built exactly 10 years apart.

3. Waldameer Park was built before Kennywood, which was built 14 years after Dorney Park.

4. No amusement park is located in a town that begins with the same letter as its name.

5. The Erie park, which is neither Kennywood nor Dorney, was built 2 years after Altoona's Lakemont Park.

6. West Mifflin was the last place to have an amusement park.

A SWEET PROFIT

Every piece of candy at the Candy Counter costs $.10. Now Mr. Sweet wants to reorder four different boxes of candy. Can you pick out the four boxes that will help him earn the most profit?

candy

Answer on page 51

Hint on page 47

Illustration: John Nez

NAME	PIECES PER BOX	DOLLAR AMOUNT SOLD	COST OF 1 BOX	PROFIT
1. Lilly's Lollies	15		$.75	
2. Mini caramels	20		$1.00	
3. Jelly beans	40		$2.75	
4. Licorice bits	10		$.50	
5. Chewy's Bubble Gum	50		$2.50	
6. Candy dots	12		$.80	
7. Tilly's Taffy	35		$2.00	
8. Tart Tarts	50		$3.00	

LIQUID BLOCKS

This is Erin's entry in the school art contest. The subject is Fun with Water. If each block holds exactly 8 ounces of water, how many gallons of water will Erin need to fill her entry?

Hint on page 47

Illustration: Jim Downer

Answer on page 51

KEEPING TRACK

It's time to total up the points from the Middle School Track Finals. Use the charts

to fill in the points earned
by each team so that you
can announce the winners.

EVENT	FIRST	SECOND	THIRD	FOURTH
3200-Meter Run	Creektown Bulldogs	Cedar Vikings	Golden Flashes	Oakville Lions
100-Meter Dash	Cedar Vikings	Golden Flashes	Creektown Bulldogs	Cedar Vikings
1600-Meter Run	Golden Flashes	Oakville Lions	Creektown Bulldogs	Cedar Vikings
70-Meter Dash	Creektown Bulldogs	Cedar Vikings	Golden Flashes	Oakville Lions
55-Meter Hurdles	Golden Flashes	Creektown Bulldogs	Creektown Bulldogs	Cedar Vikings
400-Meter Run	Oakville Lions	Cedar Vikings	Golden Flashes	Oakville Lions
200-Meter Dash	Cedar Vikings	Creektown Bulldogs	Creektown Bulldogs	Oakville Lions
800-Meter Run	Creektown Bulldogs	Golden Flashes	Oakville Lions	Cedar Vikings
200-Meter Hurdles	Oakville Lions	Oakville Lions	Creektown Bulldogs	Oakville Lions
Long Jump	Creektown Bulldogs	Oakville Lions	Oakville Lions	Cedar Vikings
High Jump	Cedar Vikings	Golden Flashes	Oakville Lions	Oakville Lions
Discus Throw	Golden Flashes	Oakville Lions	Creektown Bulldogs	Oakville Lions

1st place = 6 points
2nd place = 4 points
3rd place = 3 points
4th place = 2 points

MIDDLE SCHOOL TRACK FINALS	
1st place	
2nd place	
3rd place	
4th place	

Answer on page 51

Illustration: Rick Geary

AS YOU WERE

Sometimes it's tough to see how one number might relate to another number. But all numbers have some relationship to other numbers. See if you can fill in the blanks to complete the comparisons.

1. 2 inches is to 4 inches and 3 inches is to 6 inches as _____ inches is to 8 inches.

2. 13 inches is to 19 inches as _____ inches is to 27 inches.

3. 16 hours is to $\frac{2}{3}$ as 24 hours is to _____.

4. 10 minutes is to 1 hour as _____ is to 1 minute.

5. 5 is to 25 as _____ is to 36.

6. 1 foot is to a yard as 1760 feet is to a _____.

7. A century is to a millennium as a _____ is to a century.

8. An inch is to a foot as a _____ is to a year.

9. A quarter is to a dollar as _____ is to an hour.

10. A penny is to a dime as a dime is to a _____.

Illustration: Don Robison

Hint on page 47

Answer on page 51

TALENT TIME

A new television show is looking for a young person to be the host. The job has only two requirements:

1. The host must be between 10 and $12\frac{1}{2}$ years old.
2. The host must live 15 miles or closer to the studio (since someone from the studio has to pick up the host and drop him or her off each night).

CHANNEL 99

There are ten possible hosts in line for the job right now. Which ones meet the requirements?

1. Daniella—11 years old, lives 13 miles from studio
2. Andrew—9 years old, lives 15 miles from studio
3. Justin—144 months old, lives 16 miles from studio
4. Maxine—10 years old, lives 5 miles from studio
5. Matt—11 years old, lives 11 miles from studio
6. Bethany—$12\frac{3}{4}$ years old, lives 12 miles from studio
7. Kevin—13 years old, lives 10.5 miles from studio
8. Darby—100 months old, lives closer than Andrew
9. Rachel—Five months younger than Kevin, lives half as far away as Justin
10. Chris—144 months old, lives right next door to Kevin

Illustration: Marc Nadel

Answer on page 51

HINTS AND BRIGHT IDEAS

*T*hese hints may help with some of the trickier puzzles.

COVER
Sunflowers are $.50 each.

QUICK CALCULATION (page 3)
Column B has the total you are looking for. What number can you move to make the other two columns add up to 15?

CALL TO ORDER (page 7)
.33 is roughly the same as $\frac{1}{3}$. Lincoln is the middle man.

PERIMETERS (pages 8-9)
Add the side measurements together as you make your way around each figure. Find the perimeters of all figures first. Then fill in the letters to solve the riddle.

ON THE RUN (page 10)
Lydia ran the fewest laps. Maureen ran the most laps. All runners ran an even number of laps. One runner ran 10 laps.

CROSSWORD RIDDLE (pages 12-13)
XI is one more than X, which is 10. *Re*, *bi*, and *tri* are some prefixes you may need.

HOT DOG! (page 14)
You'll catch up if you start with Tina and Terri.

DIFFERENT DEFINITIONS (page 18)
WH is the first $\frac{1}{2}$ of WHEN. ERS is the middle $\frac{3}{5}$ of VERSE.

TICKET TIME (page 19)
Start with Sean. Which two vacations add up to a total of $750?

DIGIT DOES IT (pages 22-23)
The word *Inspector* appears in the note's greeting.

STEP BY STEP (page 25)
The first four numbers on the path are 0, 9, 4, and 13. Can you add and subtract to find a sequence?

STACKING STANLEY (page 28)
The trick is to divide the number of books in the carton by the number of books in each stack. When you come up with an even answer with no remainders, then you've found the area where the books should be stacked. For example, 152 books can be divided evenly by 19 into 8 stacks, so these books should go in area 19.

HAY, SAM (page 29)
Sam has 24 fields. $\frac{1}{2}$ of 24 is 12. $\frac{1}{4}$ of 24 is 6. Multiply the amount of gas by the number of miles the tractor gets per gallon to find how much area the tractor will cover.

CAN YOU CANOE? (pages 34-35)
When doing question 3, multiply the answer to question 1 by 2.

A SWEET PROFIT (page 40)
Multiply the number of pieces in a box by $.10 to find the dollar amount sold of each box. Subtract the cost of the box from the dollar amount sold to see how much profit Mr. Sweet will make. He will choose the four boxes with the highest profit.

LIQUID BLOCKS (page 41)
Each 8 ounces is equal to 1 cup. There are 2 cups in a pint, 2 pints in a quart, and 4 quarts in a gallon. Start by figuring how many blocks you can fill with one gallon of water.

AS YOU WERE (page 44)
This may look harder than it is. In statement 1, 2 inches is $\frac{1}{2}$ of 4. You need to find the number that is $\frac{1}{2}$ of 8. Look for relationships in the numbers within each statement.

ANSWERS

COVER
Tulip—$.05
Rose—$.10
Violet—$.20
Sunflower—$.50

QUICK CALCULATION (page 3)
Move the 9 from column C and add it to column A.

EAT 'EM UP (pages 4-5)
Toad—2,000 insects in a year
   (500 + 600 + 500 + 400 = 2,000)
Bolas spider—8 moths in a night
   (1 + 1 + 1 + 4 + 1 = 8)
Common spider—100 insects in a year
   (25 + 25 + 50 = 100)
Brown bat—600 mosquitoes in an hour
   (150 + 150 + 150 + 100 + 50 = 600)
Ladybug—5,000 aphids in a lifetime
   (1,000 + 1,000 + 2,000 + 1,000 = 5,000)

LAST COIN (page 6)

CALL TO ORDER (page 7)
A. Simple Simon had 0 pennies,
   Old King Cole had 3 fiddlers,
   and 24 blackbirds were baked in a pie.
B. .33 ($\frac{1}{3}$), $\frac{2}{3}$, 3
C. 13, 48, 50
D. Washington was the 1st President of the
   U.S.; Lincoln, the 16th; Nixon, the 37th.

PERIMETERS (pages 8-9)
What large animal can put you into
a trance?
A HYPNO-POTAMUS

ON THE RUN (page 10)
Lydia ran 2 laps. Maureen ran 10 laps.
Nancy ran 8 laps.

DOTS A LOT (page 11)

CROSSWORD RIDDLE (pages 12-13)

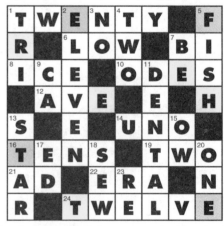

What can you find in every single yard?
THREE FEET

HOT DOG! (page 14)
Timmy—18   Tony—25
Todd—9   Terri—12
Tanya—9   Ted—24
Tina—4   Tony was the winner!

FAMOUS NAME (page 15)

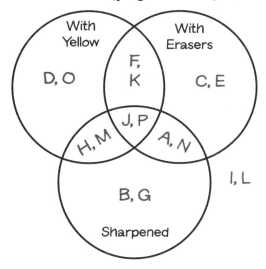

```
    A B C D E F G H I J K L
1
2   B E . T . S . Y . . .
3
4   R O S S . . . . . . .
5
6
```

BETSY ROSS

PENCIL THEM IN (pages 16-17)

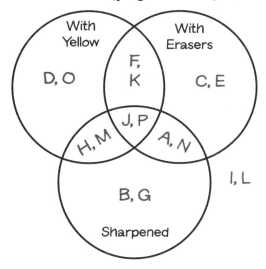

With Yellow: D, O
With Erasers: C, E
Sharpened: B, G

F, K (Yellow ∩ Erasers)
H, M (Yellow ∩ Sharpened)
A, N (Erasers ∩ Sharpened)
J, P (center)

I, L

DIFFERENT DEFINITIONS (page 18)
BASEMENT: WHAT INFIELDERS USE TO KEEP THEIR BREATH FRESH

TICKET TIME (page 19)
Jen—B   Brooke—F   Felix—C
Sean—A, D   Jeff—E

A TOUGH SPELL (pages 20-21)
Sunday, November 21

DIGIT DOES IT (pages 22-23)
Dear Inspector Digit,
You may have me in the pen, but that won't stain my career. You have no inkling where to find all 23 pens you need for evidence. Paul Point

a-1	f-15	l-9	r-10	w-11
b-7	g-8	m-16	s-22	y-6
c-17	h-21	n-13	t-14	
d-12	i-3	o-4	u-5	
e-2	k-18	p-20	v-19	

SLEEP TIGHT (page 24)

DAY	HOURS OF SLEEP	DAY	HOURS OF SLEEP
Sunday	$9\frac{1}{2}$	Thursday	$10\frac{1}{4}$
Monday	$10\frac{1}{4}$	Friday	9
Tuesday	$10\frac{1}{4}$	Saturday	$9\frac{3}{4}$
Wednesday	$9\frac{1}{2}$		

Total for the week: $68\frac{1}{2}$ hours
Number of days of at least 10 hours: 3

STEP BY STEP (page 25)

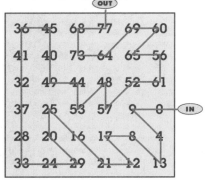

The sequence is +9, –5.

SCRAMBLED PICTURE (pages 26-27)

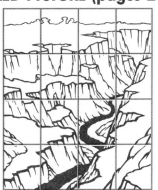

STACKING STANLEY (page 28)
276 copies of *King Minus*—Area 12
  ($276 \div 12 = 23$ stacks of 12 books each)
169 copies of *The Grapes of Math*—Area 13
  ($169 \div 13 = 13$ stacks of 13 books each)
994 copies of *The Brothers Addemup*—Area 14
  ($994 \div 14 = 71$ stacks of 14 books each)
119 copies of *Alice in Integerland*—Area 17
  ($119 \div 17 = 7$ stacks of 17 books each)
152 copies of *Great Multiplications*—Area 19
  ($152 \div 19 = 8$ stacks of 19 books each)
220 copies of *The Indivisible Man*—Area 10
  ($220 \div 10 = 22$ stacks of 10 books each)

HAY, SAM (page 29)

Sam will need to buy more gas.

She has 5 gallons of gas, each of which will cover 6 miles ($5 \times 6 = 30$ miles).

In the morning, she will do 12 fields for a total of 12 miles.

$\frac{1}{4}$ of the fields is 6. At $1\frac{1}{2}$ miles each, that's 9 more miles.

The other 6 fields are a total of 12 miles.

That makes a total of 33 miles.

MAGIC SQUARE (pages 30-31)

In this magic square, each line across, down, or diagonally adds up to 70.

$16 \div 4 =$ **4**	$9 + 7 =$ **16**	$10 + 15 =$ **25**	$63 \div 9 =$ **7**	$9 \times 2 =$ **18**	=70
$11 \times 2 =$ **22**	$24 \div 3 =$ **8**	$23 - 4 =$ **19**	$42 \div 7 =$ **6**	$5+5+5 =$ **15**	=70
$6+7+8 =$ **21**	$5 \times 1 =$ **5**	$21 - 9 =$ **12**	$18 + 5 =$ **23**	$72 \div 8 =$ **9**	=70
$9 + 4 =$ **13**	$3 \times 8 =$ **24**	$6 + 5 =$ **11**	$5 \times 4 =$ **20**	$24 \div 12 =$ **2**	=70
$2+3+5 =$ **10**	$20 - 3 =$ **17**	$16 - 13 =$ **3**	$14 - 0 =$ **14**	$13 + 13 =$ **26**	=70
=70	=70	=70	=70	=70	=70

LIBRARY LAUGHS (page 32)

$27 \div 9 = 3$	C		$8 - 6 = 2$	B
$3 \times 5 = 15$	O		$5 \times 5 = 25$	Y
$26 - 3 = 23$	W		$24 \div 2 = 12$	L
$44 \div 22 = 2$	B		$19 - 18 = 1$	A
$9 + 6 = 15$	O		$6 \times 3 = 18$	R
$50 \div 2 = 25$	Y		$36 \div 2 = 18$	R
$22 - 4 = 18$	R		$21 + 4 = 25$	Y
$30 \div 2 = 15$	O		$10 \div 2 = 5$	E
$9 + 7 = 16$	P		$5 \times 4 = 20$	T
$14 - 9 = 5$	E		$24 - 4 = 20$	T
$2 \times 10 = 20$	T			
$14 + 4 = 18$	R		COWBOY ROPE TRICKS	
$18 \div 2 = 9$	I		by Larry Ett	
$9 - 6 = 3$	C			
$7 + 4 = 11$	K			
$26 - 7 = 19$	S			

PRECISE ICE (page 33)

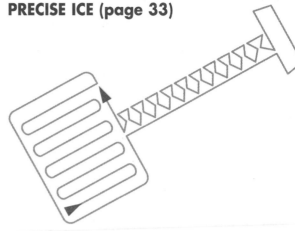

CAN YOU CANOE? (pages 34-35)

1. 6 hours, 15 minutes
2. 5 hours, 14 minutes
3. $12\frac{1}{2}$ miles

MATHMAGIC (page 36)

The first set of multiplications is to enhance the idea of the 3, 2, 1, 0! But as you probably know, any number times 0 is 0. So you're actually starting over from that point. 999 divided by 3 is 333. Subtract 12, and you're left with 321. Your friend should say, "3, 2, 1." That's when you can yell.

COLOR BY NUMBERS (page 37)